It was snowing.
"Hooray," said the children.

1

They saw Wilf and Wilma.

Wilf was sweeping the snow.

Biff had a good idea.

She made a giant snowball.

Everyone pushed the snowball.

Floppy barked and barked.

Wilf had an idea.

He wanted to play a trick.

The children made a giant snowman.

Wilf's dad opened the door.

He saw the snowman.

Wilma's mum took a photograph.

The snow fell off the roof.

"Six snowmen!" said Wilma's dad.